AIRCRAFT CARRIERS IN ACTION

Author Erik Bergaust takes his readers aboard the newest aircraft carriers in the U. S. Navy to reveal what life is like both above and below decks. The missions of modern Task Forces and the immensely complex operations necessary to carry out those missions are described clearly. Bergaust also tells the story of the beginnings of the Navy's air arm.

AIRCRAFT CARRIERS
IN ACTION

by Erik Bergaust

G. P. PUTNAM'S SONS  NEW YORK

To Bobby and Paul
— who want to
join the Navy

Photos courtesy of U.S. Navy

CONTENTS

FOREWORD

The mission of the modern U. S. Navy is so simple that it can be summed up in just four words: *deter, strike, defend,* and *control.* At the same time, these four words stand for jobs so vast, complex and important that thousands of highly trained men and millions of pieces of equipment — from the simple and useful steel helmet of a gunner to the delicate electronic devices in a missile's guidance system — are needed to carry them out.

Here is what the Navy does and what it must always be ready to do:

Deter — Through its strength the Navy shall discourage an enemy from acts against the interests of the United States, deter general war, and ensure freedom of the use of the seas.

Strike — In time of war the Navy must seek out and destroy forces which threaten our use of the seas, prevent enemy use of the seas, and transport and supply troops.

Defend — The Navy must always be ready to defend the United States against attack from the seas.

Control — In time of war the Navy must control all vital sea areas and protect shipping.

This mission today is unchanged from what it was in the days of wooden sailing ships, but the ways in which the mission is carried out are beyond the dreams of sailors of only a few years ago.

The key to the Navy's handling of all the situations that could arise under the mission set for it is the Task Force. A Task Force is exactly what it sounds like, a combination of Navy weapons brought together to handle whatever job is at hand. Whether the job is to strike enemy forces on land or sea, destroy its submarines and other undersea weapons, support a landing on its shores, mine its harbors or furnish supplies to our own land forces, there is a Navy Task Force which can meet the need. A Task Force is the single most powerful armed force in the world today.

The Task Force has another advantage. It is composed of super-weapons, each able to defend itself. It is also better able to strike and hide from enemy return blows.

This also brings up another point about the Navy in our defense picture. Should we ever be forced to fight a nuclear war, the havoc created by today's weapons striking land-based forces could not help but cause great damage to our cities and rural areas. The same weapons used against naval forces could destroy only military targets. Often such weapons would explode harmlessly in the sea.

Only bases in space could offer the same safety to the civilian population, and for some time to come a space station will be too difficult to supply. In addition, a space station satellite could not be hidden from enemy counterattack. Because such stations travel in regular orbits and therefore would be fairly easy to locate and attack, we must continue to depend on the oceans as the most practical place to maintain a large and powerful mobile defense force.

The seas also offer us the opportunity to keep our forces within easy striking range of any potential enemy country with a seacoast. By long-established international law, the waters within a few miles of any coast are open to all ships of any nation. Of course, this also poses a threat to us, because the enemy would have the same right to hide his weapons along our shores. This means that the "defend" part of the Navy's mission takes on special importance. Not only must our ships and planes clear our coasts of the enemy in time of war, but they also must control the seas along his shores to fight the enemy.

It is clear, then, that our new Navy must be ready with weapons and must also have vast and accurate knowledge of all portions of all the oceans. Some of the ways the new Navy is gaining this knowledge will be shown in the pages to come. Exciting new ways of exploring our unknown ocean beds have been developed and others are coming.

It may be that the growth of knowledge about the sea will help not only to defend us, but may also lead to new ways of mining the wealth of minerals in the seas and beneath them. Perhaps the development of underwater cargo ships which can travel on nuclear power under polar ice will also come from the Navy's efforts. Certainly a more accurate charting of the ocean floor and powerful sea currents would aid merchant shipping as well as our defense forces.

In preparing this book I have received incalculable assistance from the U. S. Navy, and from *Naval Aviation News* and many industry sources. My special thanks to the Sikorsky Aircraft Division of the United Aircraft organization, which provided some of the material and the striking cover illustration. All other illustrations are official U. S. Navy photos.

Erik Bergaust
Washington, D.C.

CHAPTER 1

GUARD AGAINST ENEMY SUBMARINES

OUR Navy's great aircraft carriers have seen much action in recent years. They were used a good deal during the Korean War, and at the moment this is being written, several of them are fighting in Vietnam. Additionally, other carriers are on station throughout the world to protect the peace.

Aircraft carriers also have been in the news during the last few years because they have played an important role in our space program. A carrier, or "flat top," is always used as the prime recovery ship for astronauts returning from their journeys in space.

Needless to say, the main function of an aircraft carrier is to carry aircraft. Yet, today's modern Navy has grouped its huge carriers into two very distinct classes based on two specific military missions. Some carriers are designed and equipped as attack vessels while others are assigned to antisubmarine warfare.

The attack carriers constitute the home base for jet fighters and attack bombers, while the antisubmarine-warfare carriers transport

The U.S.S. *Shangri-La (CVA-38)* under way off Mayport, Florida.

A close-up aerial view of the U.S.S. *Bon Homme Richard (CVA-31)*.

observation planes and helicopters equipped with sonar gear as well as weapons with which to kill enemy submarines. Sonar is a type of underwater radar used by helicopters, destroyers and other vessels to "listen" for submerged submarines.

According to today's military thinking our aircraft carriers operate in groups made up of a number of different kinds of ships, including destroyers, missile cruisers, and supply ships. Such groups are called Task Forces, and several of these are assigned to specific

Crewmen swab the deck of the U.S.S. *Bainbridge (DLGN-25)* during the first surface around-the-world cruise of a nuclear task force.

theaters of operation in the North Atlantic, the Mediterranean, the North Pacific, the South Pacific and other areas. Since almost 80 percent of our globe is covered by water, it is easily understood that the Navy Task Forces cover a lot of territory. They must be on the move all the time to keep close watch over thousands of square miles of ocean.

The aircraft carriers constitute the backbone of the Navy. Together with missile-carrying submarines and other ships designed for special missions, the widespread use of aircraft carriers has made the U. S. Navy the strongest and most powerful navy in the world. By employing aircraft carriers, the Navy can put into operation on short notice a base of jet fighters or attack bombers close to any trouble area in the world. Likewise, the use of antisubmarine carrier forces up and down our coasts provides a strong barrier against enemy submarines.

Let's go aboard a carrier and discover the duties of the sailors and pilots who are assigned to protect the peace against enemy submarines. We have selected the famous *Wasp,* because all of us know this ship so well from television and newspapers as the carrier used often to recover our astronauts. That sort of job is not, of course, the primary mission of the *Wasp;* this huge vessel is ordinarily on station somewhere as one of our most powerful antisubmarine-warfare carriers.

We're aboard the *Wasp* at sea late in the evening. The hatch at the rear of the low-ceilinged "ready room" swings open and some young men file in. They enter quietly, like lean and tired athletes returning to a locker room after a rough round on the practice field. They hang their bright-hued helmets and other gear on hooks along the bulkheads, then slump into airline-type seats set three abreast on either side of a passageway dividing the narrow room. Leaning

Crewmen of Nuclear Task Force One, sightseeing in Brazil, pause to view the Corcovado Mountain.

The U.S.S. *Wasp (CVS-18)* under way in the Atlantic.

back, they zip open the collars of their rumpled orange flight suits and wait. It is almost midnight.

The men are pilots and sonarmen of Helicopter Squadron 11 (HS-11), and their business is antisubmarine warfare (ASW). More than six hours before they had sat in the same room, somewhat less disheveled and infinitely less tired. During those hours they had undergone a 35-minute preflight briefing, sat 40 minutes on the flight deck in their Sikorsky *SH-3A Sea King* helicopters to

Pilots gather for a briefing aboard the U.S.S. *Ranger (CVA-61)*.

18

complete further preparations for the practice mission, and flown four hours (half the time hovering only 40 feet above the sea in the black of night). During the long flight, they had made numerous sonar dips, flying intricate search patterns and keeping in constant radio touch with fixed-wing aircraft and destroyers also engaged in the exercise, as well as with the *Wasp's* C.I.C. (Combat Information Center), nerve center of the whole operation.

Now, as the men wait for a half-hour debriefing, their minds leap ahead to the showers and sack time soon to come. Overhead on the flight deck several fixed-wing ASW aircraft, twin-engine Grumman *S2E Trackers,* are returning to the carrier, the rumble and thump of their cable-arrested landings clearly audible in the ready room just below.

HS-11's busy history reaches back to June 1957 and includes Caribbean, Mediterranean and eastern Atlantic cruises, as well as many nearer home. The news highlight, probably, was the squadron's recovery of astronauts McDivitt and White. The pickup was made by Commander Clarence O. Fiske, former commanding officer, and Lt. Dougles C. Ballard, with James J. Cummings operating the *SH-3A's* rescue hoist.

HS-11, with sixteen *SH-3A's* and personnel numbering about 265, is one of nine such squadrons operating with ASW carrier groups, formerly called Hunter-Killer (HUK) task groups, in the Atlantic and Pacific oceans. Two other ASW helicopter squadrons serve as Replacement Air Groups (RAG): HS-1 at Key West, Florida, and HS-10 at Ream Field, San Diego, California. The RAG squadrons train the new pilots in ASW missions, so that the pilots reach the ASW carrier forces ready to go to work.

The Naval Air Station, at Quonset Point, Rhode Island, is HS-11's shore base, while the *Wasp's* home berth is Boston. The *Wasp* is a

CVS, or antisubmarine carrier. The other ASW carriers operate out of Quonset Point and Norfolk, Virginia, on the East Coast, and from San Diego and Long Beach, California, on the West Coast. Included are such well-known vessels as the *Essex, Lake Champlain, Intrepid, Randolph, Hornet, Kearsarge, Bennington* and *Yorktown.* Each carrier spearheads an ASW group which includes aircraft, destroyers, submarines and even the support of long-range, land-based patrol planes. Thus an ASW group's capability is three-dimensional — air, surface and subsurface.

Each element of the ASW group has its own strengths and limi-

The U.S.S. *Intrepid (CVA-11)* executes a sharp turn at sea.

The U.S.S. *Kearsarge (CVS-33)* maneuvers at sea with most of her planes below-deck.

tations, so that teamwork is the key to the group's ultimate effectiveness. An airplane, with its long range and multiple sensors, may be the first to detect a sub. The helicopters, with their ability to hover and lower their sonar gear, then converge on the scene to make contact with the sub, track it, and, if possible, attack it with torpedoes. If time and distance permit, two or three destroyers will reach the area to conduct their own attack.

Vital to the team is the *Wasp's* Combat Information Center, a three-room unit amidships just below the flight deck. In the eerie

The U.S.S. *Kearsarge* leads eight destroyers into Subic Bay in the Philippines.

22

gloom of the C.I.C.'s main room, radar operators sit hunched over their scopes while red and green lights blink and illuminated wall charts cast a dim glow over the scene. "Our job here," says Commander Gordon R. Otis of Fairfield, Connecticut, a veteran of more than twenty years as a Naval aviator, "is to keep in touch with all the surface and air units through radio and radar, collecting and evaluating information and sending it to the bridge and to the admiral's headquarters."

HS-11's 46 pilots and 2 ground officers range in age from young men in their early twenties to veterans like Commander Norman H.

The U.S.S. *Lake Champlain* (CVA-39) at anchor in the harbor at Cannes, France.

The U.S.S. *Yorktown (CVS-10)* moves peacefully through quiet seas.

McLaughlin, the squadron's forty-one-year-old commanding officer, and Commander James R. Williford III, forty, the outfit's executive officer. The newer pilots, like Lt. James H. (Ned) Davis, Lt. Alex Daunis, Lt. Bob McPherson, Ensign Jack O'Brien and Lt. Tom Calkins, all have a youthful exuberance. Like their colleagues, however, they are sobered by the responsibilities of their job. They know that in an age of missile-firing submarines ASW is one of the nation's first lines of defense, and one of its most difficult. They real-

The U.S.S. *Bennington* with helicopters on the forward flight deck.

Blairsville Junior High School
Blairsville, Pennsylvania

A stern view of the U.S.S. *Bennington,* with one plane taking off at the bow.

ize, too, that day and night, in fair weather and foul, they are entrusted with some highly expensive property — their aircraft and the lives of their crewmen.

Ned Davis, a soft-spoken economics major from Lehigh University, '63, puts it this way: "We get a lot more responsibility a lot earlier than in civilian life. We take a million dollars in aircraft and equipment, plus two sonarmen in whom the Navy has already invested about $35,000 each, and hover forty feet off the water at night when you can't see your hand in front of your face." However, Davis found no civilian jobs that appealed to him, likes his new work, and hopes to make the Navy his career.

A typical sonar investment is Michael E. Malloy, a lanky six-footer from Waterbury, Connecticut. Malloy is an AX3 (AC) which translates into "aviation antisubmarine warfare technician, third class, and designated aircraft crewman." The Navy gave him thirty-six weeks of intensive training, and although he has been with HS-11 since early 1964, he's still learning — both on the job and through special courses.

"We learn the basic techniques in school," Malloy says, "but it isn't until after we get into the Fleet that we develop our skills and get the most out of our sets." On a mission, the first and second sonarmen split the sonar duty, about an hour on and an hour off, with the off-duty man handling radio messages.

Commander Williford, HS-11's scholarly executive officer, a 1949 graduate of Georgia Tech, set a world helicopter distance record by flying an *SH-3A* from San Diego to Mayport, Florida. "In addition to its primary search and attack mission," he says, "a HUK force can also provide escort for attack carriers and for convoys. The helicopters give defense in depth by getting out far ahead of the destroyers and the carrier. We try to keep a sub in the center of the helicopters until we, or the destroyers, or the S2E's can make an attack."

Recently, so-called hot-fuel missions have added an hour to the SH-3A's normal mission duration of four hours. "During these missions," says Commander Williford, "we return to the carrier after three hours, refuel using a pressurized system, which takes only a couple of minutes compared to fifteen or twenty by gravity fueling, and then take off for another two hours. We don't even shut down the engines. One advantage is that if you make a contact late in a flight you can stay with it and not have to launch another aircraft."

One of HS-11's most seasoned ASW men is its operations officer, Lt. Comdr. Walter H. (Bud) Brown, whose ASW experience includes flying patrol planes, trackers and helicopters as well as duty in the C.I.C. "Much of the time we practice only segments of a complete ASW exercise," he explains. "We may know where the sub is and do just the finishing segment — the attack. Or we may do a screening operation, or a night operation. Every so often, though, we take on a full ASW problem, one that requires round-the-clock work for thirty-six hours or even as long as ninety-six hours."

An ASW exercise, from take-off to landing, is a precise procedure with little left to chance. The helicopter pilots and sonarmen, for example, are first briefed by an ASW officer on the tactical situation; the kinds of subs to look for; other units of the carrier participating; and their own positions in relation to the other aircraft and surface vessels. If a sub has been detected its location (or datum) is given to the crews. Next comes a weather forecast for both the search area and the shore-based alternate, or "Bingo," landing field.

A man from ASWEPS (Anti-Submarine Warfare Environmental Prediction System) brings word of vital concern to the mission. "He talks weather, too," says Lt. Comdr. Brown, "but he's considering the water conditions, temperatures, the depths of the various temperature layers beneath the surface. From these he predicts sonar ranges and effectiveness. Earlier, destroyers and helicopters have lowered thermometers into the water to obtain such bathythermograph, or BT, readings. The surface layer may be as deep as five hundred feet, or much less. Knowledge of subsurface conditions is vital because sonar signals are deflected by the temperature changes and subs can hide under the layers."

With takeoff time approaching, the mission's flight leader takes over, giving headings, altitudes, formation positions, and mission stations. He covers safety, preflight checks, emergency procedures, job assignments. His aim is an orderly flight with no confusion, regardless of what develops.

As the helicopters take off they are under control of the carrier's air officer, or "air boss," in the carrier's control tower. They are soon switched, however, to control by the C.I.C., whose radio and radar provide central coordination of the mission. From then on it's a fox and hounds chase as the ASW force uses all its skills to detect, track and "kill." The kill is made with low-power practice depth charges which cause no damage but which the sub crew can hear. When "killed," the sub sends up an air bubble, or a flare at night, to acknowledge its demise.

At night or under instrument flight conditions the helicopter's sonar dips are fully automatic. The pilot simply pushes a button and his automatic flight control system takes over, carrying him through an automatic transition in speed and decrease in altitude to an automatic hover at 40 feet off the water.

"Night dipping," says Brown, "is the ultimate in our field — putting the aircraft on automatic and hovering with no horizon."

What if the weather socks in zero-zero? Again, planning prevents

A crewman repairs a hydraulic leak on the nose wheel of a plane on board the U.S.S. *Independence* (CVA-62).

confusion. "The aircraft climb to assigned altitudes with 500 feet (of) vertical separation," says Commander Brown. "They use TACAN (Tactical Air Navigation), which gives them the bearing and distance to the carrier, and fly a holding pattern about five miles from the ship. Then they are brought in one by one by CCA (Carrier-Controlled Approach), which is similar to an airport's GCA, or ground-controlled radar approach."

How well the bad-weather system works was recalled by Commander Frank Ford, the *Wasp's* assistant air officer. "Earlier this year we were searching for survivors of an Air Force radar picket plane which had ditched at sea," he said. "It was so foggy you could hear the helicopters hovering off the fantail, but you couldn't see them. They had come in so low they picked up the ship's wake and followed it in. But we got them aboard. We even brought in a land-based Coast Guard *HH-52A* (Sikorsky *S-62*) which needed fuel."

Aircraft need maintenance, and good maintenance demands experienced men. Lack of such experience, chiefly because of a rapid turnover in personnel, gives HS-11 a king-sized headache. "We have a 75 percent turnover each year in our maintenance force," says Lt. William H. Carder, squadron maintenance officer. "It's not like it used to be when we kept men eight or ten years."

The complaint is echoed by HS-11's maintenance chief, Harry A. King, of Sharon, Connecticut, a towering, straight-talking man, typical of the veteran chiefs who reputedly "run the Navy." Says King, "We could keep eighty-five percent aircraft availability without strain if we had the people we need. But most of our people are new — and we're shorthanded as well as short-talented. It's a problem prevalent all through the services."

Despite the problem, HS-11 is meeting its ASW commitment, but only through long hours and extra effort by all hands.

What of the future prospects and needs of ASW? Aboard the *Wasp* one finds a high authority in Rear Adm. William N. Leonard, since June 1965 Commander of Carrier Division 14, and before that in high positions with the U. S. Atlantic Fleet and with NATO.

Admiral Leonard, a much-decorated fighter pilot of World War II and, in 1948, commander of the Navy's first jet aircraft squadron, sees antisubmarine warfare as "not merely a single problem, but a whole world of military interplay."

"We are organized," he says, "to contend with the opposition in many different ways, which is characteristic of any good military program. There is a role in this for aircraft off the beach, there is a role for patrol aircraft, a role for carrier-based aircraft, for surface ships, and even for our own friendly subs — first in helping us train and even in hunting enemy subs.

"Within each role are special weapons. The carrier's ability to base helicopters is one of its great strategic strengths. The helicopter with the magic of zero ground speed is a very useful implement which we exploit to its fullest. The helicopter used to be a very fragile, fair-weather, daylight vehicle. But now, in its second generation, it is an all-weather aircraft asking no special treatment from anyone. Today we feel we can use helicopters under conditions that would stop all other aviation — and we've done it."

Admiral Leonard sees the helicopter squadron as "a highly respected member" of the CVS group. "We operate helicopters like interceptors," he says. "They are directed to the target area by the carrier and other surface ships. Then, operating in a third dimension, they tell us what they hear under the water."

Combining this capability with all the other weapons and sensors available to the HUK force provides a broad capability, he believes. "To repeat," he says, "we have many different ways of getting at the problem."

A repair crew takes a breather during training aboard the U.S.S. *America* (CVA-66).

Admiral Leonard predicts a growing usefulness for the helicopter in ASW. "We see the helicopter today as such an able vehicle that we know it can do more than it is doing," he says. "We hope to see the day when it will carry additional sensors and become even more valuable. Now we have only the capability of dipping sonar; we'd like to see it carry other sensors as well."

Another veteran Naval aviator, Capt. Gorden E. Hartley, skipper of the *Wasp,* believes the recent improvements in helicopters and fixed-wing aircraft have brought "marked increases in our ASW capability." But he describes the missile-carrying nuclear sub as a "real tough nut to crack — a problem not yet licked."

ASW's future is a favorite subject among HS-11's pilots during bull sessions in the *Wasp's* air-conditioned wardroom. There, over a hot chocolate or coffee, in the rare moments when they are not being briefed, debriefed, taking correspondence courses or tracking submarines, they kick around the topic.

"Why not," asks Lt. Charles E. Oyler, squadron personnel officer, "design the helicopter specifically to land on the water in calm seas and dip its sonar? That would avoid some of the night hovering, would use less fuel, and would be a lot easier on the nerves."

"And why not," adds another, "make the cable longer and get the sonar dome way down through the thermal layers?"

In the view of those close to ASW technology, the answers to these and other questions will come as ASW capabilities continue to grow. Meanwhile, the men of HS-11 and other ASW squadrons, both rotary and fixed-wing, continue the practice that they hope will make them perfect in a task which in wartime would demand nothing less.

CHAPTER 2

PROUDEST SHIPS IN THE FLEET

MEN aboard the Navy's attack carriers also see a lot of action. The pilots are specially trained to take off from and land on the limited flight deck under rough weather conditions. Sometimes they have a difficult time finding their way back to base, and sometimes they are shot down over vast areas of water.

This happened to Commander William N. Donnelly, who parachuted from his crippled jet after attacking targets in Vietnam, deep in the Gulf of Tonkin. Donnelly, Commanding Officer of Fighter Squadron 154, spent forty-five hours in the water before being rescued by an Air Force Rescue Amphibian *HU-16* (piloted by Maj. Kenneth L. Shook). He was found about 10 miles west of a small island located 135 miles southeast of the North Vietnamese capital of Hanoi.

Navy aircraft from the carriers *Hancock, Yorktown,* and *Coral Sea* conducted a massive two-day search for the missing pilot, scanning a great portion of the Gulf of Tonkin. Approximately ninety-

The U.S.S. *Hancock (CVA-19)* running at high speed in the South China Sea.

five planes participated in the intensive search which involved a total of 190 flight hours.

Donnelly was first spotted by the pilot of an *F8D Crusader* operating from the carrier *Hancock.* The pilot of the *Crusader* requested rescue assistance from the Air Force, which was standing by with a rescue plane. Donnelly stated the rescue plane was the "prettiest sight" he ever had seen.

Prior to his recovery, he had been seen last pulling off the target after attacking a radar installation on a small island. No transmissions were heard from him that he was in any trouble or that he was leaving his aircraft. He had landed in the water about four miles west of the target island, his biggest concern being whether or not anyone had seen him eject.

After landing in the water he discovered the life raft leaked, and he had to inflate it orally about every twenty minutes. During the first night of his ordeal, around midnight, Commander Donnelly heard the sound of a ship's screws churning through the water. The sound appeared to be coming from various directions, which indicated a search pattern. About two hours later, the downed pilot observed a ship's searchlight being flashed intermittently on and off, scanning the murky darkness. However, the ship turned away and he no longer could see its beam.

Nearly an hour later Donnelly again sighted the ship heading in his direction and using the searchlight intermittently, as before. He believed it was an enemy ship. As it came closer to him, he slipped into the water. Though painfully injured, he turned his raft over himself for camouflage. (The life raft, brightly colored when in an upright position for easy spotting from the air, has a dark-colored bottom to blend with the color of the water.) The ship came within 300 yards of Donnelly twice that night, and twice he had to slip

Crew members aboard the CVA-19 guide an F8 Crusader onto the catapult.

into the water and turn the raft over himself to keep from being spotted.

At the first break of dawn Commander Donnelly saw the ship. It was an escort type heading in a northerly direction at an estimated speed of 20 to 25 knots. It showed no flag and during the previous night had displayed no running lights. Throughout the day and night Donnelly observed nothing unusual, although he said later that he could hear aircraft overhead.

When the pilot was rescued by the Air Force plane, he was suffer-

A gun crew is silhouetted aboard the U.S.S. *Boston (CAG-1)* during a practice alert.

A lookout aboard the U.S.S. *Saint Paul (CA-73)* is muffled against cold weather.

ing from shock. On the way back to Da Nang from the pickup scene, an Air Force crew member rendered first aid, put Donnelly's dislocated shoulder back in its socket, and gave the commander some soup which helped to bring him out of shock. He was listed as being in good condition when he arrived in Da Nang. Commander Donnelly was awarded the Purple Heart by General W. C. Westmoreland, Commander, U. S. Military Assistance Command, Vietnam.

Commander Donnelly's experience is not unusual for carrier pilots in the Navy, but it is seldom that a downed pilot must spend so

A lookout scans the Saigon River from aboard the U.S.S. *Oklahoma City (CLG-5)*.

many hours in the water before he is picked up by a rescue plane or a helicopter.

Before, during, and after an attack by carrier aircraft, the flat top itself is a busy place. There is action everywhere, with more than two thousand men pitching in.

The ship's crew members are concerned with the operation of the ship itself, its navigation, correct attitude in the wind, speed. Radar men, radio operators, and flight operations personnel are busy keeping track of the airplanes and of any enemy action. The carrier's antiaircraft gun and lookout personnel are on their stations, and

A telephone talker aboard the U.S.S. *Oklahoma City* in the Saigon River.

A student Navy diver in deep-sea gear practices making repairs underwater.

members of the ground crews are getting ready to receive the home-coming planes for refueling or repair work. In the ship's interior, doctors and nurses are preparing to aid any injured pilots. Search planes and helicopters are warming up their engines and are on constant standby for distress signals from the fighter pilots. The carrier's Commanding Officer is on his bridge; responsible for all operations running smoothly and safely, he cannot rest for a moment.

Life on board a carrier — even when it is not participating in an attack — is almost like life in a city. It never dies down. Someone is always on duty or at work, and the carrier operates very much like a self-sustained city. It has its own bakery, hospital, library, theater, basketball court, and so on. It is equipped to spend several months at sea without outside support of any kind.

Most of our aircraft carriers are famous for one or more battles or for participating in operations far from the United States. Actually, it is possible to write a volume about each of the Navy's carriers, but we'll limit ourselves to a few examples. One that stands out is the *Hornet*, now the eighth Navy ship bearing that name.

There is little detailed information available on the exploits of four of the first five *Hornets*, but what knowledge we have of their missions and accomplishments for the U. S. Navy shows them to have been among the most distinguished fighting ships in American Naval history.

The first *Hornet* was a sloop equipped at Baltimore, Maryland, by the Continental Marine Committee in the fall of 1775. On February 13, 1776, armed with ten long 9-pounders and commanded by Capt. William Stone, she joined Commodore Esek Hopkins' squadron in the Delaware River.

Under the command of Capt. John Nicholson in January 1777, the *Hornet* was ordered to escort a convoy of merchantmen "fairly out to sea." This was no easy task, because the British had vessels blockading their route. But the *Hornet* managed to evade them and bring the merchants safely to sea.

On her return from this cruise, the *Hornet* was attached to Commodore Saltonstall's squadron in the Delaware River. This proved to be a fatal assignment. With the fall of the forts guarding the approaches to Philadelphia on November 17, 1777, the American vessels under Saltonstall were left without protection. Therefore, Capt. Nicholson was given orders to destroy the *Hornet* to prevent the ship from falling into enemy hands.

A fire-fighting crew sprays foam and water on a burning aircraft.

Purchased at Malta in 1805, the second *Hornet* was a ten-gun sloop. She was commissioned by Lt. Samuel Evans and assigned to Commodore Rodgers' squadron in the Mediterranean during the Tripolitan War.

In March 1805, the *Hornet* was ordered to Bomba, on the coast of Tripoli, to aid General William Eaton in the proposed attack on Derne. She joined two other ships on April 25, and two days later the little squadron ran within range of the shore batteries, anchored, got springs on their cables and opened fire. In about an hour the Turks were driven from their guns and the shore was cleared for General Eaton's party to advance by land. The capture of Derne prompted the Bashaw of Tripoli to agree to the American commodore's terms for peace. In 1806 the ship was sold out of service at Charleston, South Carolina.

A 440-ton, brig-rigged sloop of war, the third *Hornet* was launched at Baltimore, Maryland, on July 28, 1805. She was a beautiful little vessel, modeled after the designs of French naval ships, and she carried an armament of eighteen 32-pounder carronades and two long 9-pounders on a flush spar deck, with neither poop nor topgallant forecastle.

On June 21, 1812, three days after the declaration of the War of 1812, the *Hornet* put to sea in company with the *President, Congress,* and *United States.* On July 9, a British privateer came within range of the patrolling squadron. The *Hornet* chased, overtook, and captured her. A fortnight later the *Hornet* claimed one more prize when the squadron took after another enemy vessel in the same waters. The ships then returned to Boston where they anchored on August 31.

The *Hornet*'s last cruise was under the command of Master

Commandant Otho Norris. On February 5, 1829, she foundered in a heavy gale and was lost with all hands off Tampico, Florida.

The fourth *Hornet* was a five-gun schooner bought at Georgetown in 1813. She mounted one long 18-pounder and four 18-pound carronades. Between 1813 and 1820, she was commanded successively by Lt. Lewis B. Page, Lt. Jesse Wilkinson, Lt. James Ramage, and Lt. John P. Zantzinger. She was sold out of service in 1820.

Captured off New Inlet, North Carolina, during the Civil War on October 28, 1864, by the U.S.S. *Calypso* and *Eolus,* the fifth *Hornet* was an iron side-wheel steamer of the third rate. She was taken into service under her original name of *Lady Sterling,* but on June 17, 1865, the Navy Department ordered her renamed *Hornet.*

Under the command of Acting Master Joseph Avant, the *Hornet* was ordered to accompany the *Rhode Island* to Havana, Cuba, in October 1865, for the purpose of receiving the surrender of the Confederate vessel *Sam Stonewall.* On her return from this cruise she was laid up in ordinary at the Navy Yard, League Island, Pennsylvania, on December 18, 1865. On June 26, 1869, she was sold out of service for $33,000.

Purchased on April 6, 1898, from Henry M. Flagler for $117,500, the sixth *Hornet* was originally the steel steam yacht *Alicia,* built by Harlan and Hollingsworth at Wilmington, Delaware, in 1890. Vertical inverted triple-expansion engines of 800 horsepower made her capable of a speed of 15 knots.

The *Hornet* was fitted out at the Navy Yard, New York, on April 12, 1898, by Lt. James H. Helm, and joined the United States Fleet off Havana two weeks later. Then on May 7, with a battery of three 6-pounders, two 1-pounders, and four machine guns, she engaged enemy artillery in a Spanish-American War engagement at the entrance of Matanzas harbor. The following month, the *Hornet* joined a division of the Fleet off Rebecca Shoal Light and assisted in convoying army transports from that point to Daiquirí.

With the end of the war with Spain, the *Hornet* was ordered out of commission at the Navy Yard in Norfolk, Virginia, on October 18, 1898. In December of the same year she was given to the North Carolina Naval Militia for drill and instructional purposes. Two years afterward, she was brought back to Norfolk where she acted as a tender to the receiving ship *Franklin* from 1904 to 1906. Then she was laid up in ordinary until March 18, 1911, when she was stricken from the Navy register and ordered out of the service.

Authorized by the Naval Expansion Act of May 17, 1939, the keel of the seventh *Hornet* was laid on September 25, 1939, by the Newport News Shipbuilding and Dry Dock Company, at Newport News, Virginia. For the thirty-one years previous, the Navy had been without a ship to carry on this fighting name.

Launched on December 14, 1940, and christened by Mrs. Frank Knox, wife of the Secretary of the Navy, the carrier was placed in commission at the Naval Operating Base at Norfolk, Virginia, on October 20, 1941, under the command of Capt. Mark Andrew Mitscher, who was later succeeded by Capt. Charles Perry Mason.

Before the bombing raid against Tokyo, Japan, on April 18, 1942, Brig. Gen. Jimmy Doolittle and his flyers took off from the flight deck of the *Hornet*, which had carried the twin-engine bombers to within 800 miles of the Japanese coast.

In the battle of Santa Cruz Island on October 20, 1942, the *Hornet* took her last stand against the enemy and perished in a blaze of gunfire.

Using bucket brigades after the fire-fighting apparatus was destroyed, the *Hornet* was taken in tow and led from the battle area.

But before she could be led away safely, subsequent attacks damaged her still more. At the height of one attack, a 1,000-pound bomb pierced her deck and lodged in a room next to the ordnance compartment. An ordnance chief entered the compartment in the dark and disarmed the bomb.

Eventually, after ten hours of attack, the order was given to torpedo the *Hornet* in order to preclude any possibility of her falling into enemy hands. After other vessels had rescued all but 129 of her complement of 2,900 men, two U.S. destroyers torpedoed and sank her. So, in the final analysis, the Japanese themselves couldn't sink her.

When news came that the seventh *Hornet* had been sunk, the Navy decided to transfer the name to *CVS-12*, the support aircraft carrier that was originally to be called *Kearsarge*. On August 30, 1943, ten months after the *CV-8* had been lost, the eighth *Hornet* was launched. In the Norfolk Navy Yard at Portsmouth, Virginia, on November 29, 1943, she was commissioned by the same sponsor and patrons of honor who had participated in the launching of her predecessor.

After being commissioned, the *Hornet* then took a limited shakedown cruise to Bermuda and back to prepare her for immediate service with the Pacific Fleet. During this exercise she conducted gunnery, fueling and various calibration tests as well as flight operations.

Arriving at Pearl Harbor on March 4, 1944, she became part of Task Force Fifty-eight. She earned the Presidential Unit Citation and also received seven battle stars on the Asiatic-Pacific Service Medal from March 1944 to January 1945.

The *Hornet* participated in raids on Palau, Yap, Truk, the capture and occupation of Saipan, and the battles of Surigao Strait, northern Luzon, and Formosa. She served as a troop transport from 1945 to June 1946 during Operation Magic Carpet. She then was decommissioned after a glorious record of operations during the latter part of World War II.

In May 1951 she was brought from San Francisco, California, to the Brooklyn Navy Yard, where conversion began on July 15, 1951. The conversion covered a period of twenty-seven months. This work made her a sister ship to the U.S.S. *Oriskany (CVA-34)*.

The U.S.S. *Oriskany (CVA-34)* moving slowly upriver.

The U.S.S. *Oriskany,* viewed from the forward port quarter, after conversion work was completed.

She went on a round-the-world cruise during late 1954 and early 1955. In late 1955 the *Hornet* underwent modernization in the Puget Sound Naval Shipyard at Bremerton, Washington. There she received the angled flight deck and hurricane bow.

In 1956, 1957 and again in 1958 she made Far East cruises. During her 1958 cruise the *Hornet* did such an outstanding job that she received the Battle Efficiency "E" and the Aviation Safety Award.

The *Hornet* left the United States on April 4, 1959, for another Western Pacific cruise, her first as a support carrier.

To prove the greatness of the name *Hornet* through the history of the U.S. Navy, the ship once again won the coveted Battle Efficiency "E." She also demonstrated her excellence in engineering by winning the Engineering "E" for the fiscal year 1959-60 for the second consecutive year. All totaled, the *Hornet* and her air group won ten awards for all-around excellence in 1960.

She has won four Battle Efficiency "E's" to date, carrying on the grandeur of the name she bears. In addition, the *Hornet* again won the Engineering "E" in 1962 to wrap up an outstanding year which included a Far East deployment.

The *Hornet* is just one of many carriers with glorious and proud records. Another is the attack aircraft carrier U.S.S. *Ticonderoga*, the tenth Essex-class carrier built for the Navy. She is nicknamed the *Big T, Tico,* and *Ti,* and is named for the Battle of Fort Ticonderoga which was fought during the Revolutionary War. The *Tico* is the fourth naval vessel to bear this name. Her keel was laid February 1, 1943, and she was commissioned May 8, 1944.

The *Tico* saw action in several naval battles in World War II as part of Task Force Thirty-eight. She struck against Japanese defenses in the Carolines, Leyte, Luzon, Okinawa and on the Japanese mainland.

Off the coast of Taiwan on January 21, 1945, a suicide plane or *kamikaze,* came out of the sun and clouds, attacking without warning. It crashed through the flight deck and its bomb exploded above the hangar deck.

The *Ticonderoga* appeared an easy target with flame and smoke rising hundreds of feet in the air. Other suicide planes attacked in succession. Three were downed by the fighting carrier's gunners. Despite their valiant defense a second *kamikaze,* although struck many times in the air, hit the carrier from the starboard side near the island, or superstructure. Its bomb exploded next to the island, starting severe fires and causing many casualties. In little more than two hours all the fires had been brought under control and were

A flier's view of the flight deck of the U.S.S. *Ticonderoga (CVA-14).*

View of the U.S.S. *Ticonderoga* under way, with aircraft clustered at the bow.

then extinguished. The *Tico* was brought safely to Ulithi, in the Caroline Islands, January 24, 1945.

The *Ticonderoga* had a total of 345 casualties, of whom 12 officers and 131 men were killed or missing. Of the remainder, 32 officers and 170 men were injured.

After emergency repairs the *Tico* received further refitting at Bremerton, Washington. Repairs were made rapidly and she was again on the firing line in May 1945. She participated in the final assaults against the Japanese Empire.

In March 1946, the *Ticonderoga* was placed in the Bremerton group of inactive reserves. Brought out of reserve in 1952, she was taken around Cape Horn to the New York Naval Shipyard. After exercises in the Mediterranean, the *Tico* went back to the shipyards, this time at Norfolk, Virginia. A new angled flight deck was added and she was redesignated a CVA, or attack carrier of the Oriskany class. In April 1957 she returned to the Pacific Coast.

The *Ticonderoga* completed her fifth deployment to the Western Pacific as part of the U.S. Seventh Fleet on July 15, 1963.

While operating in the Pacific, the *Ticonderoga* has won many commendations and awards, foremost of which is the Navy's highest peacetime award, the Battle Efficiency "E." This honor the *Tico* has won three years in a row in competition with all of the attack carriers in the Pacific.

CHAPTER 3

HOW DOES AN AIRCRAFT CARRIER WORK?

HOW big are the aircraft carriers? How much and what kind of equipment are on board? How powerful are a carrier's engines? To find the answers to these and many other questions about how a carrier works, we shall study in detail some of the newer carriers.

Let's begin with the *Constellation,* the sixth and largest Forrestal-class aircraft carrier to join the Fleet. This carrier is 1,047 feet long, has a width at the main (hangar) deck of 129 feet, a maximum extreme width at the flight deck of 252 feet, and a height from keel to flight deck of 97 feet. The full load displacement is approximately 75,000 tons. The propulsion plant can develop over 200,000-shaft horsepower, giving the ship a speed of more than 30 knots. An evaporator plant can produce approximately 265,000 gallons of fresh water a day and the electric plant is designed to handle a total electric load of almost 3 million watts.

The flight deck is approximately 4.1 acres in area. The two-acre area for parking and repairing aircraft is the main (hangar) deck. Four deck-edge elevators are installed for handling planes between the

A catapult operator gives the "go" signal to launch an E18 tracer aboard the U.S.S. *Constellation (CVA-64).*

flight and hangar decks. Each has a lift capability of 89,000 pounds. There are four steam catapults for launching aircraft and twenty-eight aircraft fueling stations distributed on the main and flight decks. The ship has two escalators, which travel at a speed of 90 feet per minute, to carry pilots dressed in flight gear from the ready rooms below deck to a flight-deck position, where they board their planes.

The *Constellation* has two anchors weighing 30 tons each. The chain for each of these anchors is 180 fathoms, or 1,080 feet, long, and each link in this chain weighs 360 pounds. The ship has two rudders weighing 45 tons each.

The ship normally accommodates about 4,100 officers and men, but in wartime it has berthing facilities for about 4,600. The crew has numerous comforts. The ship's air-conditioning system has the capacity to air-condition completely two Empire State buildings. Each man has an individual berth with reading light and foam rubber mattress. Each berthing area has a recreation space with lounge chairs and writing tables.

The *Constellation* is armed with guided missiles instead of conventional antiaircraft guns. Making up this component of her armament are Terrier missile batteries, capable of launching the surface-to-air Terrier guided missiles automatically in salvos or singly from dual-arm launchers. Traveling at supersonic speed, Terrier rides the beam of its guidance radar to ranges far in excess of conventional anti-aircraft shells. It intercepts its target with the deadly accuracy afforded by automatic tracking of the target by the radar beam. The Terrier round, including missile and booster, is approximately 27 feet long and 14 inches in diameter. The booster initiates launch and accelerates the missile to operating speed, at which time the expended booster separates and falls away, leaving the missile to continue on its guidance path. Terrier's self-contained motor sustains the missile at supersonic speed for the remainder of powered flight. On board the *Constellation*, Terrier is part of an automatic weapons system that detects and evaluates targets, selects the weapon to be used, loads the launchers, and fires in a matter of seconds. The incorporation of several guidance radars gives the ship the capability of engaging several airborne attackers at the same time.

In constructing the *Constellation*, more than 2,000,000 pounds of ½-inch-size welded metal, 185 miles of piping lines, and 300 miles of electric cable were used. The telephone installation is a fully automatic dial system.

Fireproof and fire-resistant materials have been used throughout the *Constellation*. This includes deck covering and all fabrics used in furnishings. More than 917,600 square feet of fiber-glass board were installed in the hull for thermal and soundproof insulation. Sound insulation was fitted around all noisy spaces, such as fan rooms, motor generator rooms and control rooms. Thermal insulation was fitted around all living and working areas.

The ship has a post office, three barber shops, a shoe repair shop, a tailor shop, a laundry and a dry cleaning shop. Food service facilities include two bakeries, six galleys, two butcher shops, an ice cream plant, a special diet kitchen, and two vegetable-preparation rooms. Over 13,000 meals a day are served to the ship's officers and men.

Medical facilities include two hospital wards, two quiet rooms and two isolation wards, with accommodations for a total of 84 patients. In addition, there is an operating room, a dressing room, a psychiatric consultation room, a pharmacy, a general examining room, an eye, ear and nose-examining room, and four dental offices.

Let's take a look at another superaircraft carrier, the *Kitty Hawk*. It is equipped with the world's largest elevators.

Manufactured by the Westinghouse Electric Corporation's elevator division in Jersey City, the four deck-edge elevators are powerful enough to speed the Navy's heaviest jet bombers up to the flight deck within fifteen seconds. Each elevator is large enough to hold 2,000 persons, or two-thirds of the *Kitty Hawk's* entire crew.

Operating at top speed, the four elevators combined are able to feed the flight deck with four 40-ton bombers every minute, bringing them up from the hangar deck located about thirty-six feet below. Jet fighter planes also ride to the flight deck on the elevators, which were purchased by the Navy for $5,000,000.

Should the ship's electric power fail, there would still be enough pressure in each elevator's hydraulic system to raise one more plane to the flight deck. The elevator platforms are designed to remain stable, and would not dump a plane into the sea if any one of the platform's four suspension points were shot away or destroyed.

Longer by 23 feet than the largest deck-edge elevators on any ship afloat, the 52-foot-wide platforms of the *Kitty Hawk* are uniquely shaped to speed unloading of the plane at the flight deck. Instead of the conventional rectangular shape, the platforms are 85 feet long on the outboard side and 70 feet long on the inboard side, with a total of 3,880 square feet. Platform weight is 310,000 pounds. Maximum capacity is over 89,000 pounds, including 9,000 pounds for plane-handling equipment.

A 60-foot-long hydraulic engine with a horizontally positioned plunger more than 3 feet in diameter and over 18 feet in length pulls the suspension cables up and down through a pulley arrangement. The force developed on the plunger reaches 1,300,000 pounds.

Oil under pressure is supplied to the cylinder from pressure tanks. Pressure is maintained in these tanks by four hydraulic pumps which in turn are driven by four 225-horsepower electric motors.

Three of the elevators are on the starboard side of the ship and

The U.S.S. *Kitty Hawk (CVA-63)* tests its atomic washdown equipment while at sea.

one on the port side. In ferrying planes between the hangar and flight decks, fifteen seconds are required for each phase of the loading, lifting, unloading and descending cycle.

Communications is a big problem aboard an aircraft carrier. Obviously, it is important that the officers keep in touch with every part of the ship at all times, and this is done by telephone. The 500-line, automatic-dial telephone system aboard the superaircraft carrier *Kitty Hawk* uses a 715-telephone network that provides complete shipboard communications, as well as ship-to-shore service when the carrier is in port.

The automatic switchboard — heart of the system — handles up to seventy-five calls at one time. Mounted in lightweight, shock-resistant cabinets, this switching equipment provides standard dial service plus several priority features. An "executive right-of-way" feature may be given to important stations so that urgent calls can cut in on any phones that are busy. By dialing "211," emergency priority service to the quarterdeck or pilot house can be obtained.

Three special phones are used in the *Kitty Hawk* installation. A desk type, which can be bolted down, has been installed in cabins and office areas. For bulkhead or desk side-mounting a rugged, 17-pound, wall-type phone is used. Weather decks are equipped with splashproof phones mounted in aluminum enclosures. Bulk-head and outside phones have red-light devices to illuminate the dials when the ship is darkened. All telephones have locking latches which prevent the handset from jumping off the cradle during the roll and pitch of the sea, or from battle damages.

Power supply for the installation is from a generator, with a 24-cell battery supplement designed to give emergency service for several hours if needed. Other features include specially powerful ringing equipment to assure that a telephone ring can be heard in noisy locations.

When the carrier is in port, a cordless manual switchboard con-nects the ship-to-shore telephone facilities. It is equipped with eight shoreline trunks and can handle three teletype land lines.

The U.S.S. *America* is the Navy's newest attack carrier and the first warship of this name to be commissioned into service with the U. S. Navy.

The *America* was contracted for by the Newport News Shipbuilding and Dry Dock Company at Newport News, Virginia, on November 25, 1960, and her keel was laid on January 9, 1961. She was launched and christened by her sponsor, Mrs. David L. McDonald, wife of the Chief of Naval Operations, on February 1, 1964. The *America* was placed into commission at the Norfolk Naval Shipyard, Portsmouth, Virginia, on January 23, 1965.

The first ship to bear the name *America* was a 74-gun ship of the line laid down in Portsmouth, New Hampshire, in May 1777. However, the launching of the greatest warship planned for the young Revolutionary Navy was delayed until November 1782 by a lack of funds and skilled shipbuilders.

During the last stages of her construction, the Continental Congress assigned the Revolutionary War's greatest naval hero, John Paul Jones, as the prospective commanding officer. This man, later called the father of the U. S. Navy, outfitted her but was denied his command. In September 1782, just a few months before her scheduled launching, Congress presented the *America* to France as a replacement for the *Magnifique,* which had been lost by grounding in Boston Harbor. The ship which was to have sailed the oceans of the world as the U.S.S. *America* sailed instead for France and service in the French Navy in June 1783, retaining her original name.

Other ships since the Revolutionary War have taken the inspiring name, *America.* Although none were classed as warships, all served with honor and dignity in their respective fields.

One of these, a schooner yacht, was built in 1851 for Commodore John C. Stevens of the New York Yacht Club. This 111-foot yacht earned an enviable reputation in world yachting circles. In 1852 it defeated thirteen crack British yachts in a race around the Isle of Wight and became the first winner of yachting's still coveted America's Cup. During the Civil War, the Confederacy obtained the speedy yacht and pressed her into service as a blockade runner. She was later scuttled, retaken by Federal forces and refitted at Port Royal, South Carolina. She then served the Union as a blockader and finished the Civil War as a training ship at the U. S. Naval Academy. She was purchased by a civilian in 1873 and presented to the Navy Department in 1921 as a relic. The yacht was stationed at the Naval Academy and remained there until scrapped in 1945.

A twin-screw, 660-foot steamship, the S.S. *America,* was built in Ireland in 1905 for the Hamburg-American line. She was taken into the U. S. Navy as a troop transport in 1917. By 1921, this ship was back in service as a passenger liner with the United States Lines and was operating in the North Atlantic. She was seriously damaged when she caught fire during a modernization period, but was reconditioned and laid up from 1931 to 1940. She was pulled out of retirement in 1940 and put into service as an Army troop transport.

The most recent *America* is the 723-foot United States Line passenger liner *America,* built at the Newport News Shipyard in 1940. She made her maiden voyage to the Caribbean as a civilian liner and was then converted into a troop transport and renamed *West Point.* After World War II she returned to Newport News and was reconverted for service as a passenger liner with the United States Lines. The ship was sold to foreign shipping interests in November 1964 and her name was changed to *Australis.* The S.S. *America* spent her final days under the American flag at a pier alongside her successor, the U.S.S. *America,* at Newport News.

As brief as her own history may be, the present U.S.S. *America* can look back on a line of worthy predecessors which have performed admirably under that name. As the years progress, this warship will add many glowing pages to the illustrious history of her

The flight crew rigs a crash barrier during training aboard the U.S.S. *America*.

own name, the United States Navy, and the United States of America.

The U.S.S. *America* measures 1,047 feet in length and, though a warship, is similar to a floating city. Within her hull are medical and dental facilities, a movie theater, post office, closed-circuit television and radio stations, a newspaper office, printing shop, police and fire departments, library, chapel, shoe repair and tailor shop, soda fountains and many other services normally available in an average small city.

Since the *America's* primary mission is the launching and recovery of aircraft, her flight deck is immense. Measuring 252 feet wide and covering 4.57 acres, this flight deck is equipped with four steam-operated catapults capable of launching a total of eight aircraft per minute. These aircraft can be recovered back aboard the *America* at the rate of two per minute.

The four 150-ton aircraft elevators used to raise and lower these planes between the flight deck and the gigantic hangar bay contain an area of 3,880 square feet. They are large enough to hold a normal suburban lot, complete with house and landscaping.

From her keel to her mast, the U.S.S. *America* is as tall as a 23-story building. Her superstructure, or island, is as tall as a 10-story building and was constructed initially in the center of the flight deck. It was later moved to its present position, 102 feet away, by means of a crawler crane and sliding ways.

The electronic equipment installed aboard the *America* varies in weight from less than one ounce to over 23,000 pounds. The total radiated power of the ship's electronic systems is equal to that of approximately 200 powerful commercial radio stations operating simultaneously. The potential electrical capacity of the *America* is sufficient to supply the needs of a city with a population of more than 1,000,000.

Among the *America's* electronic equipment is the revolutionary Naval Tactical Data System (NTDS). This compact computer system collects tactical data from the radar and communications systems and can complete an instruction in only 20 millionths of a second, or 50,000 instructions per minute. The communications network aboard the ship includes, 1,400 telephones. The switchboards for this complex intraship system occupy nearly 4,000 square feet.

America's powerful boilers can generate 200,000 horsepower and can drive the ship through the water at speeds in excess of 30 knots. The ship is equipped with four 5-bladed propellers, each weighing nearly 35 tons and measuring 22 feet in height. Two anchors, one located on the extreme bow and the other on the port bow, each weigh 60,000 pounds. The 30-inch links in the anchor chain each tip the scales at 391 pounds.

America's evaporators have the capacity to distill 280,000 gallons of sea water daily. This provides enough fresh water to service 1,400 homes. The air-conditioning plant has a total capacity of 1,400 tons. The ship is furnished with 4,965 berths, 488 secretary-bureaus, 740 wardrobes, 314 book racks, 190 flat-top desks, and approximately 2,400 chairs. There are nearly 24,350 light fixtures.

The 128-foot-tall radar mast that towers over *America's* superstructure is hinged at the base and can be reclined at a 45-degree angle across the flight deck. This permits the ship to pass under low bridges that would normally block her passage. With her air group embarked, the *America* has a total complement of nearly 5,000 officers and men. Her six modern galleys serve 15,000 meals each day and are open most of the day and night.

CHAPTER 4

PAST, PRESENT AND FUTURE

THE U. S. Navy has 24 giant-size aircraft carriers in operation today. They are in action throughout the world, in every ocean, performing a constant watch. Billions of dollars have been spent by American taxpayers over the years to keep these ships up to date and for replacements as some of them became too old. All of the carriers in the Navy today are fitted with the most modern equipment, planes and weapons systems. But in 1910, when the Navy's air arm began with meager funds and know-how, few people could have dreamed of the Navy's growing to what it is today.

Jules Verne, author of startling science fiction during the last half of the 19th century, would have relished some of the sketches, plans, and ideas for "aeroplanes" that crossed the desk of Capt. W. Irving Chambers in 1910. Captain Chambers had recently been assigned as Assistant to the Secretary's Aid for Material, and was given the collateral duty of liaison between the Navy and the swelling number of letter writers who were eager to advance their own schemes involving aviation.

Less than seven years earlier the Wright brothers had launched their pusher biplane at Kitty Hawk, North Carolina, in a brief but impressive flight. In the intervening years, advocates of aviation fought for recognition — and money.

At first, the Navy's interest in aviation was skeptical, if not openly discouraging. Twelve years before Chambers entered the picture, "the Joint Army-Navy Board to Examine [Samuel] Langley's Flying Machine" had been formed at the urging of Assistant Secretary of the Navy Theodore Roosevelt. A Navy member reported favorably on it to the General Board. But the Secretary, upon the advice of another bureau in the Navy Department, decided "the apparatus as (it) is referred to pertains strictly to the land service and not to the Navy."

On at least two important occasions between then and 1910, the Navy participated in or observed the fledgling "apparatus" in flight — the 1907 Jamestown Exposition and the 1908 tests by the Wright brothers at Fort Myer, Virginia. But the Navy Board held to the attitude that "aeronautics" had "not yet achieved sufficient importance in its relation to naval warfare" to warrant Navy support.

Not until 1910 was specific action taken to alert the Navy to the potentials of aviation. In one incident, pioneer aviator Glenn H. Curtiss successfully flew a prizewinning flight between Albany and New York. At its conclusion, he prophesied publicly:

"The battles of the future will be fought in the air. The aeroplane will decide the destiny of nations." And he added, "Encumbered as (our big war vessels) are within their turrets and military masts, they cannot launch air fighters, and without these to defend them, they would be blown apart in case of war."

The "battleship controversy" was on, magnified by the publicity of a competitive press. Curtiss added weight to his argument by a series of tests near Hammondsport, New York, in which he lobbed 15 out of 22 "bombs" into targets as large as and shaped like battleships.

There was a rumor that France was building an aircraft carrier. More to the point, a growing group of enthusiasts, the U. S. Aeronautic Reserve, asked the Navy to appoint a representative who would handle aviation matters. Since this civilian organization enjoyed semiofficial status, Captain Chambers was assigned to handle all correspondence on the subject.

Chamber's job proved far from easy. He was given no space to work in, no clerical help, no operating money, no authority, and precious little encouragement. Despite this, he later wrote to Lt. T. G. Ellyson, "I am endeavoring to start an office of aeronautics here in such a way that things will run smoothly without having them all get into one Bureau and made a mess of as was the submarine question."

In October 1910, the Navy was invited to send a corps of midshipmen to Halethorpe, Maryland, where an aviation meet was to be held. Instead, Chambers and two other officers were sent; for the Navy, Chambers, and Naval aviation, it was a fortunate decision. There he met Curtiss and the Curtiss-trained pilot, Eugene Ely. At that time, the Navy had neither an aircraft nor a designated pilot. In a series of startling tests Chambers, Curtiss and Ely demonstrated that this situation would soon have to change.

Several problems nagged Chambers. There was no conclusive proof, for instance, that it was feasible to launch and land aircraft at sea. If there was to be any future for aviation in the Navy, he had to demonstrate that aircraft could be operated by, and were important to, the Fleet. Navy, military and civilian officials, were still apathetic about the program and gave it token and grudging cognizance — when they treated it with any degree of seriousness at all.

The first test was prompted by plans of a German merchant line to launch a plane from one of its ships in order to speed up its mail service. Chambers was appalled that such an advance might be made by a foreign power when the airplane had been developed by the United States. He obtained permission to make a similar launch attempt from the deck of the cruiser *Birmingham*. The Wright brothers were contacted, but they demurred; Ely was eager.

A temporary wooden platform was erected on the *Birmingham* at the Norfolk Navy Yard. The German line, mindful of the Navy's experiment, moved up its target date in an effort to be the first to launch, and thereafter bask in the honor of claiming a significant aeronautical first. Luck was not with them, however. An accident aboard ship, caused by a careless workman, forced a delay of the experiment.

Chambers' plan went ahead without a hitch. On November 14, 1910, the *Birmingham* pulled into the waters off Hampton Roads, Virginia, in company with three torpedo destroyers. Aboard were pilot Ely and his biplane. The weather was unsatisfactory; visibility was limited by a low cloud cover, and there were light showers mixed with hail.

Ely was not discouraged. He slipped into the seat of his aircraft near three in the afternoon and signaled his handlers to let loose. The plane roared off the platform, took a dangerous dip when it left the platform, then swung into the air. In the takeoff, the skid framing and wing pontoons of the plane struck the water, nearly aborting the flight. The prop tips were splintered and water splashed over Ely's goggles. This brief baptism and the steady rain blanketed his vision, and for a moment he swung dizzily in the air. Finally, he spotted the sandy beaches of Willoughby Spit and touched down, ending a 2½-mile flight.

The flight was an extraordinary success, but Chambers tempered his jubilance with native conservatism. Said he: "After (Ely) had demonstrated his ability to leave the ship so readily, without assistance from the ship's speed, or from any special starting device, such

71

as that formerly used by the Wright brothers, my satisfaction with the results of the experiment was increased."

He admitted to being worried before the experiment: "The point of greatest concern in my mind, carrying out the original program, was the uncertainty of stopping the ship or changing the course in time to prevent running over the aviator in case he should land in the water.

"His demonstration that an aeroplane of comparatively old design and moderate power can leave a ship in flight while the ship is not underway points clearly to the conclusion that the proper place for the platform is aft. An after platform can be made longer, will not require a lessening of the stays of any mast, and its essential supports can be so rigged as a permanent structure of a scout cruiser as to cause no inconvenience in arranging the other military essentials of the ship's design."

News of the feat inspired a New York Navy Yard worker to design a light movable platform for installation above the turrets in battleships for the purpose of launching aircraft at sea. Some Navy officials were enthusiastic, but Chambers was not quite so ready for this innovation. "Recognizing the practicability of Quarterman Joiner (E. C.) Keithley's idea," he wrote, he could "not contemplate the use of aeroplanes from turret ships in the immediate future."

Chambers' reasoning was cautious. As a result of the *Birmingham* flight, he did not think it necessary to launch aircraft into the wind. He had already gone on record as supporting the placement of the platform in the aft section of the ship, and saw no reason to take a different stand. The safety of pilots was another determining factor: he feared they would be run over by the ship if the plane, forced to ditch, landed forward of the carrier.

Though Ely's flight opened a few Navy eyes, it did not loosen the Navy's purse strings. At this time, Glenn Curtiss offered to teach a Naval officer the mechanics of flying, absorbing the expense himself. Chambers recommended the immediate approval of the plan, and Lt. T. G. Ellyson was ordered to Curtiss' San Diego camp. A series of experiments followed in conjunction with the pilot's training.

Chambers, immensely pleased with the *Birmingham* launching, was now interested in proving the practicality of landing a plane aboard a Naval warship. Another platform was constructed at Mare Island, California, and permission was obtained to install it on the armored cruiser U.S.S. *Pennsylvania.* While the vessel was anchored at San Francisco on January 18, 1911, Ely launched his plane from a shore airdrome.

"There was never a doubt in my mind that I would effect a successful landing," Ely is quoted as saying in a March 1911 Naval Institute *Proceedings* article. "I knew what a Curtiss biplane could do, and I felt certain that if the weather conditions were good there would be no slip."

A simple arresting gear had been installed on the ship's platform. It consisted of twenty-two weighted lines stretched across the deck. On Ely's plane, a number of special hooks were fitted, designed to catch the lines as the plane made its rollout. In event the jury-rigged experimental arresting gear failed, a canvas screen was fitted to the end of the platform as an emergency stop.

The landing was, of course, a complete success, and Chambers was now armed with more ammunition in his battle to prove the feasibility of employing aircraft at sea. He vowed to take every opportunity to emphasize this fact to officers in the Fleet.

Just thirty-one days after the *Pennsylvania* landing, Curtiss taxied a seaplane from his North Island base to the same ship, then in San Diego Harbor. The plane was hoisted aboard, returned to the water, and taxied back to its base. This experiment indicated the eventual liberation of aircraft from shore bases, a necessary advancement if the aeroplane was ever to join the Fleet.

The Navy ordered its first aircraft the following May. Naval aviation in the United States had been born through the efforts and enthusiasm of a few individuals.

In the next forty years — from 1910 to 1950 — naval aviators and aircraft carriers wrote some of the finest chapters in U.S. military history. Many excellent aircraft carriers were built, and they were constantly improved and increased in size.

On June 25, 1950, North Korean forces invaded the Republic of Korea. Two days later President Harry S. Truman announced he had ordered sea and air forces in the Far East to give support and cover to Republic of Korea forces, and he ordered the Seventh Fleet to take steps to prevent an invasion of Formosa. On July 3, carrier aircraft went into action in Korea. The U.S.S. *Valley Forge*, with Air Group Five, and the British carrier H.M.S. *Triumph*, operating in

A C-130 aircraft takes off from the U.S.S. *Forrestal (CVA-59)*.

the Yellow Sea, launched strikes on airfields, supply lines and transportation facilities around Pyongyang, northwest of Seoul.

On July 12, 1951, the Navy Department announced a contract for a new large aircraft carrier (*CVB-59*), to be built at Newport News. On July 30, Congressional action approved the contract. A joint resolution from Capitol Hill proclaimed:

"Be it resolved that when and if the United States completes construction of the new aircraft carrier known as the *United States*, the construction of which was discontinued April 23, 1949, or the aircraft carrier authorized in Public Law 3, Eighty-Second Congress, first session, it shall be named the *Forrestal*."

At Newport News the new carrier was designated Hull Number 506. Her keel was laid on July 14, 1952.

Charles P. Roane, Supervising Naval Architect, Aircraft Carrier-Type Branch, Bureau of Ships, commented on the *Forrestal* in the November 1952 *Journal of the Bureau of Ships:*

"The *Forrestal* incorporates all of the developments from the other carriers, plus those learned from the *United States*. The increase in size of the *Forrestal* over the *Midway* class comes about as a normal development in aircraft carrier design. With four catapults instead of the usual two and four airplane elevators instead of the usual three, aircraft operations from this ship will be greatly improved.

"The new design was planned to meet added requirements, such as the servicing and starting of jet aircraft, maintaining the electronic appliances on the aircraft in a ready-to-go condition while the plane is on the deck, blending of aircraft fuels to get a fuel which can be used in jets without sacrificing the gasoline capacity, and a flush deck where the navigating bridge can be lowered or raised to suit operating conditions. Stacks comparable to the *Ranger* will be used. New type steels, the result of years of development, will go into the construction."

The U.S.S. *Midway* (CVA-41) at sea.

The flush-deck design had barely left the drawing board before it was changed. This design was advanced to provide optimum landing area and to eliminate the hazard of island superstructure offered by the axial deck. At the end of World War II, however, the British had developed the angled-deck concept, and they operated lightly constructed twin-engine attack planes from the marked-off deck of a British carrier. U. S. Navy pilots conducted similar tests on the *Franklin D. Roosevelt,* and the decision to modify the flight deck of a U. S. carrier was made. Accordingly, the *Antietam* was designed, landings and takeoffs were made using a variety of aircraft, and a final detailed report on the evaluation of the "canted," or angled, deck revealed that the operational trials had met with a high degree of success.

As a result of these experiments, the Navy ordered a redesigning of the deck and operating arrangements on the *Forrestal* and all future carriers, as well as structuring of many of the existing carriers during scheduled modernization periods.

When Secretary of the Navy Dan A. Kimball announced the awarding of a contract to the Brooklyn Naval Shipyard for the construction of the U.S.S. *Saratoga* (*CVA-60*), he said it would be similar to the *Forrestal.* But design improvements in machinery since *Forrestal* installation were ordered to give the *Saratoga* a somewhat higher speed.

"The importance attached to this carrier [*Saratoga*] by the Navy

The U.S.S. *Franklin D. Roosevelt* (CVA-42) with a deckload of warplanes.

The U.S.S. *Saratoga* (CVA-60) leaving Mayport, Florida.

Department," Secretary Kimball said, "is emphasized by the Navy's sacrifice of other combatant ships in the 1953 program in order that a second large carrier can be added to the Fleet.

"Although the ships sacrificed are urgently needed to augment the battle readiness of the Fleet, the Navy decided that the need for the large aircraft carrier is even more urgent in terms of national security."

The *Forrestal* was launched on December 11, 1954 and was christened by Mrs. James Forrestal. The ship was commissioned at the Norfolk Shipyard on October 1, 1955. The carrier had an overall length of 1,036 feet, a width of 252 feet, and nearly four acres of flight deck. She displaced 59,650 tons, had a horsepower rated at over 200,000, and a speed of over 30 knots. Four steam catapults were installed. She had a complement of 3,500 officers and men, including the air group.

Assistant Secretary of the Navy (Air) James H. Smith, Jr., spoke at the commissioning ceremonies. "If our way of life is to survive," he said, "we must maintain these two alternate military postures: the first is to maintain a powerful and relatively invulnerable reprisal force which will signal a potential enemy to stop, look and listen before he risks an all-out atomic war. The second is to insure that we ourselves will not be forced to change the character of a limited war because of fear of ultimate defeat in a series of them. Fortunately, we need not maintain a completely separate set of forces for each posture. In this ship and the variety of aircraft she can ser-

Two F3H Demon fighters are catapulted simultaneously off the flight deck of the U.S.S. *Saratoga.*

vice we combine the two, and we add the multiplier of the ability to appear quickly at any one of the many far-flung trouble spots. This is economy of force, achieved without sacrifice of our objectives."

The U.S.S. *Saratoga* was christened at the New York Naval Shipyard on October 8, 1955. A few token feet of water were splashed into the new ship's dry dock to "launch" her officially. She was essentially similar to the *Forrestal* but was designed to develop considerably more horsepower. She was commissioned April 14, 1956.

Her sister ship *Ranger (CVA-61)* had one outstanding difference in design to distinguish her when she was commissioned August 10, 1957. The angle of the after flight deck was altered slightly, giving her an overall length of 1,046 feet, as compared to the 1,039 of the *Forrestal*. Another innovation, an all-welded aluminum elevator, was installed on the port side, replacing the conventional steel types used on other *Forrestal*-class carriers. To expedite her building, work had been started in a smaller dock. About four months later, when the *Forrestal* was launched, the partially completed *Ranger* hull was floated into the larger facility.

CVA-62, the U.S.S. *Independence,* was constructed in Dry Dock 6 of the New York Naval Shipyard, her stem at the head of the dry dock to facilitate material delivery over a truck ramp leading from the head of the dock to the hangar deck at the stern. The island and associated sponson were not installed in order to avoid blocking off the large traveling crane. In August 1958, the extraordinarily complex job of transferring her to Dry Dock 5 was accomplished smoothly and efficiently.

The *Independence* was commissioned at the New York Naval Shipyard on January 10, 1959, the fourth carrier of the *Forrestal* class to join the Fleet.

The *Kitty Hawk (CVA-63)* and the *Constellation (CVA-64)*

The U.S.S. *Kitty Hawk* in the Pacific with the coast of Oahu, Hawaii, in the back-
ground.

were designed essentially along the *Forrestal* lines, but they developed into a separate class, the *Kitty Hawk* class. The major difference is missile capability. Both *CVA-63* and *CVA-64* are armed with
Terriers. The fuel capacity in the *Kitty Hawks* is a little greater than
the *Forrestals*, while aircraft fuel capacity is a little less. The angled
part of the flight deck is some 40 feet longer, and the catapults and
elevators have greater capacities. The U.S.S. *America (CVA-66)* has
an even longer angled deck than any of the predecessors.

On February 4, 1958, Secretary of the Navy William B. Franke
announced that the world's first nuclear-powered aircraft carrier was
to be named the U.S.S. *Enterprise.* On that same day, the keel of the
carrier was laid at Newport News.

On September 24, 1960, Adm. Arleigh Burke, Chief of Naval
Operation, delivered an address during launching ceremonies, in
which he described the new carrier.

"This new *Enterprise*, the largest ship ever built, of any kind, by any nation, will be the eighth Navy ship to proudly bear that name. Her forbears have left an enviable record, a record of courageous, distinguished service.

The U.S.S. *Enterprise* with a plane "spotted" on the flight deck.

Bow-on view of the U.S.S. *Enterprise* with Phantom 11's and F8U Crusaders on its forward section.

Four A4D's flying in formation over the U.S.S. *Enterprise (CVA-65).*

"We are looking at a major advance in the art of nuclear engineering. . . . The problems which were solved, the know-how that was developed in order to build this ship, represent a tremendous contribution to our knowledge of the military and industrial uses of nuclear energy.

"Her eight powerful nuclear reactors would enable the *Enterprise* to cruise twenty times around the world without refueling. Her great endurance and her advanced hull design would allow the ship to make this extraordinary journey at sustained high speed, exploiting to its utmost the seagoing advantage of mobility."

From the very first it was obvious that designers and builders of Newport's hull No. 546, the *Enterprise*, had hit the jackpot. Rear Adm. F. S. Schultz, Assistant Chief of the Bureau of Ships, noted that for the first time, the customary builder's trials of a major com-

Crew members play volley ball on the hangar deck of the U.S.S. *Enterprise*.

The U.S.S. *Enterprise*, escorted by the nuclear-powered guided missile cruiser *Long Beach*, cruises the Mediterranean.

bat ship had been eliminated, and the ship was presented to the Navy for acceptance trials on her first trip to sea.

The *Enterprise* returned to the shipyard after her six-day Navy acceptance trials in the Atlantic. A giant broom was affixed to her masthead to signify a clean sweep of the trials. Capt. W. M. Ryan, President of the Naval Board of Inspection and Survey, stated:

"The ship generally performed in an excellent manner. The cleanliness and upkeep were outstanding. The fine workmanship throughout the ship reflects great credit upon all hands concerned with its building. Like all new ships there are bugs which must be worked out, but we feel that there is nothing that cannot be overcome."

The plant for the nuclear-powered aircraft carrier was designed under the supervision of Vice Adm. Hyman Rickover.

Designated *CVA (N)-65*, the *Enterprise* was commissioned on

November 25, 1961, at Norfolk, with Capt. V. P. dePoix commanding. The world's first nuclear-powered carrier has a length of 1,040
feet and an extreme breadth of 252 on the flight deck. Each of the
four deck-edge elevators cover about 4,000 square feet. The *Enterprise* is the first carrier to have elevators for pilots in lieu of escalators. She displaces 85,350 tons.

The communications equipment on the carrier is believed to be
the largest assortment ever assembled on any ship. In addition to
more than 1,800 telephones, there is a complex of numerous radio
circuits, teletypes, a pneumatic tube arrangement to carry messages
from one station to another, and numerous public address systems,

A crew member aboard the U.S.S. *Enterprise* preheats an A5A Vigilante.

Armed warplanes cluster at the base of the tower of the U.S.S. *Enterprise*.

several of which have speakers throughout the ship. The *Enterprise* is the first ship of the U.S. Navy's Atlantic Fleet to have the Navy Tactical Data System installed.

The *Enterprise* is equipped with four steam-driven catapults with an energy potential of 60,000,000 foot-pounds. With this power, an aircraft weighing 78,000 pounds can be accelerated to 160 miles per hour from a standing start in a distance of 250 feet. All of the aircraft aboard can be launched at the rate of one every fifteen seconds while using all four cats.

The size of the *Enterprise*'s island structure was dictated by the size of the two radar screens that flank each of its four sides. This newly developed radar system is the most powerful to be installed on a floating platform, according to Capt. dePoix. Its far-reaching, three-dimensional capability is enhanced by its height above the water line. The silhouette is distinctive.

Propulsion and control characteristics of the ship offer great tactical flexibility. There are four rudders, one almost directly astern of each propeller. This provides excellent maneuverability at all speeds as well as tactical diameters in turns which compare with much smaller ships.

She can launch a strike on the enemy from one position, recover, and launch another twenty-four hours later from an unpredictable position more than 800 miles away from her previous strike position. This ability will constantly be a factor in causing the enemy to utilize protective forces that could be deployed elsewhere.

If a show of force is required, the *Enterprise* can be on station in a remote area in a shorter period of time than any other ship in the Fleet. In 1965 the *Enterprise* joined other Naval forces in the Gulf of Tonkin, and before long became very active in the Vietnam War. Sometimes as many as 138 jet fighter sorties were flown against Communist targets in one day.

The *Enterprise* may well be called a forerunner of tomorrow's combat ships. A second nuclear-powered carrier is being considered by the Navy, and — who knows — in the not-so-distant future all of the Navy's big ships may be powered by atomic reactors.

NAME SOURCES FOR NAVY SHIPS

You may often have wondered how the Navy picks names for its ships. The following listing shows you that the Navy has some strict rules to go by in this respect. The next time you see a naval vessel, check its name against this listing and you will be able to tell what kind of a ship you have seen.

BATTLESHIPS

BB Battleship	States of the Union

CRUISERS

CA Heavy Cruiser	Cities in the United States and capitals of U. S. possessions and territories
CAG Guided Missile Heavy Cruiser	Same as above
CG Guided Missile Cruiser	Cities in the United States
CL Light Cruiser	Cities in the United States and capitals of U. S. possessions and territories
CLAA Antiaircraft Light Cruiser	Same as above
CLG Guided Missile Light Cruiser	Same as above

AIRCRAFT CARRIERS

CVA Attack Aircraft Carrier	Famous ships formerly on the Navy list and important U. S. battles, operations and engagements
CVL Small Aircraft Carrier	Same as above
CVS ASW Support Aircraft Carrier	Same as above

DESTROYERS

DD Destroyer	Deceased Naval, Marine Corps and Coast Guard personnel, Secretaries and Assistant Secretaries of the Navy, Congressmen associated with Naval affairs, and inventors
DDE Escort Destroyer	Same as above
DDG Guided Missile Destroyer	Same as above
DDR Radar Picket Destroyer	Same as above
DL Frigate	Same as above
DLG Guided Missile Frigate	Same as above

SUBMARINES

SS Submarine	Fish and denizens of the deep
SSB Fleet Ballistic Missile Submarine	Distinguished Americans
SSG Guided Missile Submarine	Fish and denizens of the deep

AMPHIBIOUS WARFARE VESSELS

AGC Amphibious Force Flagship	Mountains in the United States and possessions
AKA Attack Cargo Ship	U. S. counties and astronomical bodies
APA Attack Transport	U. S. counties; deceased commandants and officers of the Marine Corps, signers of the Declaration of Independence, famous men and women in history; famous men of foreign birth who aided our country in struggle for independence
APD High Speed Transport	Deceased Naval, Marine Corps and Coast Guard personnel
APSS Transport Submarine	Fish and denizens of the deep
IFS Inshore Fire Support Ship	Weapons
LPD Amphibious Transport, Dock	Cities named for explorers and developers of the United States
LPH Amphibious Assault Ship	U. S. battles
LSD Dock Landing Ship	Places of historical interest
LSM Medium Landing Ship	Small cities in the United States (Pop. 2,500 to 10,000)
LSMR Medium Landing Ship (Rocket)	Rivers in the United States
LST Tank Landing Ship	Counties in the United States

MINE WARFARE VESSELS

DM Minelayer, Destroyer	Former destroyers
MCH Minehunter, Coastal	Birds
MMF Minelayer, Fleet	Former monitors
MSC Minesweeper, Coastal (non-magnetic)	Birds
MSCO Minesweeper, Coastal (Old)	Birds
MSF Minesweeper, Fleet (Steel Hulled)	Birds and general word classification
MSO Minesweeper, Ocean (Non-magnetic)	General word classification

PATROL VESSELS

DE Escort Ship	Deceased Navy, Marine Corps and Coast Guard personnel
DEG Guided Missile Escort Ship	Same as above
DER Radar Picket Escort Vessel	Same as above
PC Submarine Chaser (173')	Small cities in the United States (Pop. 2,500 to 10,000)
PCE Escort (180')	Same as above
PCER Rescue Escort (180')	Same as above
PCH Submarine Chaser (Hydrofoil)	Cities in the United States
PCS Submarine Chaser (136')	Small cities in the United States
PF Patrol Escort	Cities in the United States
PY Yacht	Former U. S. ships, gems and general word classification

INDEX

(Figures in italics indicate pages on which illustrations occur.)

92

THE AUTHOR

ERIK BERGAUST has written a variety of popular books on rocketry and space themes. He has been a project engineer for several missile and aeronautical engineering companies, as well as editor of several rocket and space magazines. He served as president of the National Capital Section of the American Rocket Society in 1957 and was the founder and first president of the National Space Club.

Other In Action Books
by Erik Bergaust and William O. Foss

COAST GUARD IN ACTION

HELICOPTERS IN ACTION

THE MARINE CORPS IN ACTION

SKIN DIVERS IN ACTION

OCEANOGRAPHERS IN ACTION